Contents

Numbers to 20

Look at these numbers.
Count and say them aloud.

1 one	2 two	3 three	4 four	5 five
6 six	7 seven	8 eight	9 nine	10 ten
11 eleven	12 twelve	13 thirteen	14 fourteen	15 fifteen
16 sixteen	17 seventeen	18 eighteen	19 nineteen	20 twenty

Steady practise this

1 Count the stars. Write how many there are on each flag.

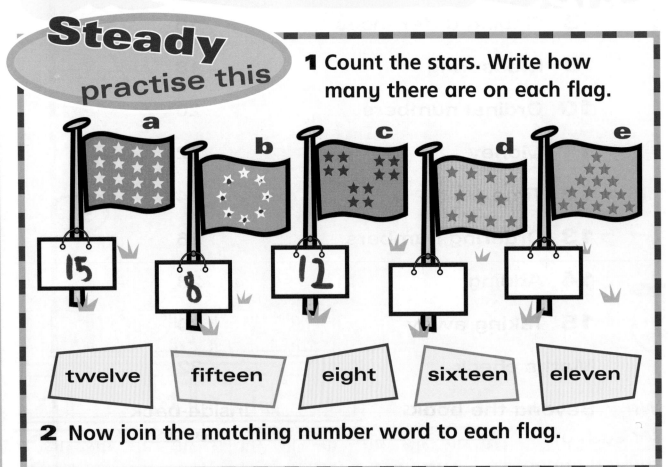

a 15   b 8   c 12   d   e

twelve   fifteen   eight   sixteen   eleven

2 Now join the matching number word to each flag.

ANSWERS: 1 (a) 16; (b) 8; (c) 12; (d) 11; (e) 15
2 twelve → (c); fifteen → (e); eight → (a); sixteen → (b); eleven → (d)

Numbers to 20

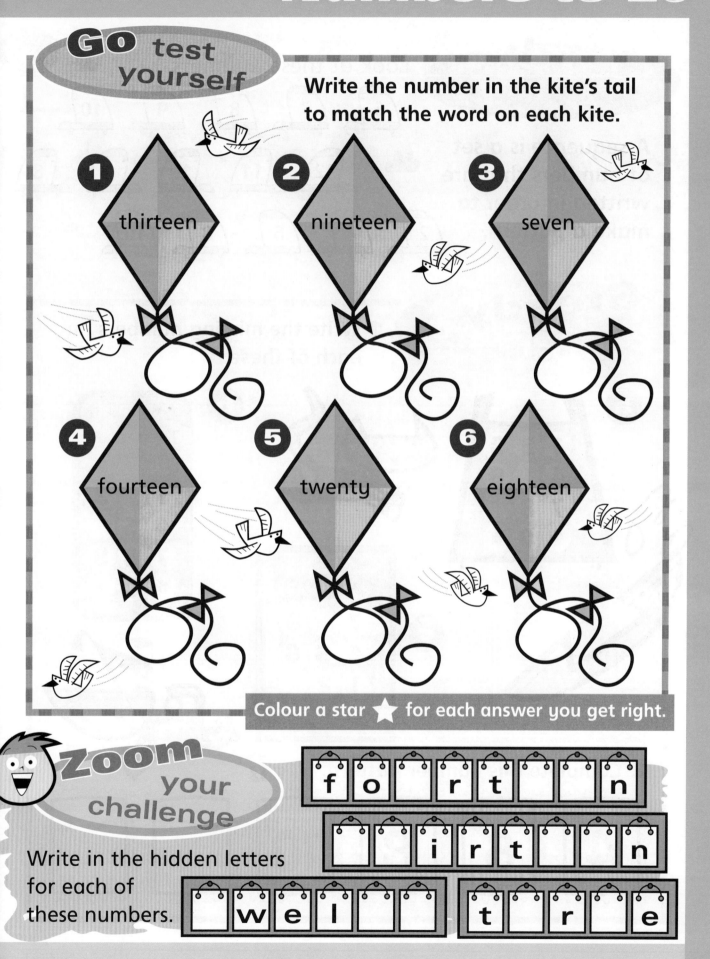

Go test yourself

Write the number in the kite's tail to match the word on each kite.

1. thirteen
2. nineteen
3. seven
4. fourteen
5. twenty
6. eighteen

Colour a star ⭐ for each answer you get right.

Zoom your challenge

Write in the hidden letters for each of these numbers.

f o _ r t _ n

_ _ i r t _ n

w e l _ _

_ t _ r e

ANSWERS: (1) 13; (2) 19; (3) 7; (4) 14; (5) 20; (6) 18

3

Counting sequences

Ready
read this

A sequence is a set of numbers that are written in order to make a pattern.

Look at these:

6 7 8 9 10

12 11 10 9 8

2 4 6 8 10

Steady
practise this

1 Write the missing numbers on each of these.

a

1 2 3
4 ○ 6
7 8 ○
* 0 *

b

1 ○ 3
4 5 ○
7 8 9
* 0 *

c

0

7 ○ 9
4 5 6
1 2 ○
0 + −

2 Complete this number pattern.

4 6 8 10 ☐ ☐

4

Counting sequences

Fill in the missing number in each set of doors.

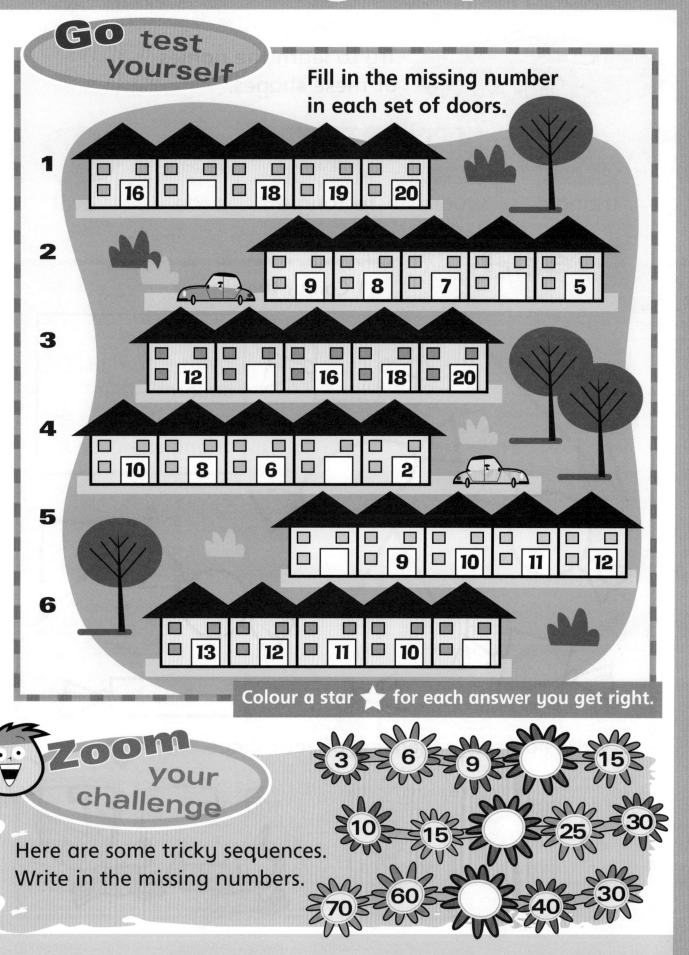

1. | 16 | | 18 | 19 | 20 |

2. | 9 | 8 | 7 | | 5 |

3. | 12 | | 16 | 18 | 20 |

4. | 10 | 8 | 6 | | 2 |

5. | | 9 | 10 | 11 | 12 |

6. | 13 | 12 | 11 | 10 | |

Colour a star ⭐ for each answer you get right.

Zoom your challenge

Here are some tricky sequences. Write in the missing numbers.

3 6 9 ◯ 15

10 15 ◯ 25 30

70 60 ◯ 40 30

ANSWERS: (1) 17; (2) 6; (3) 14; (4) 4; (5) 8; (6) 9

5

Flat shapes

Try to learn the names
of these shapes.

triangle   square   rectangle   circle   oval

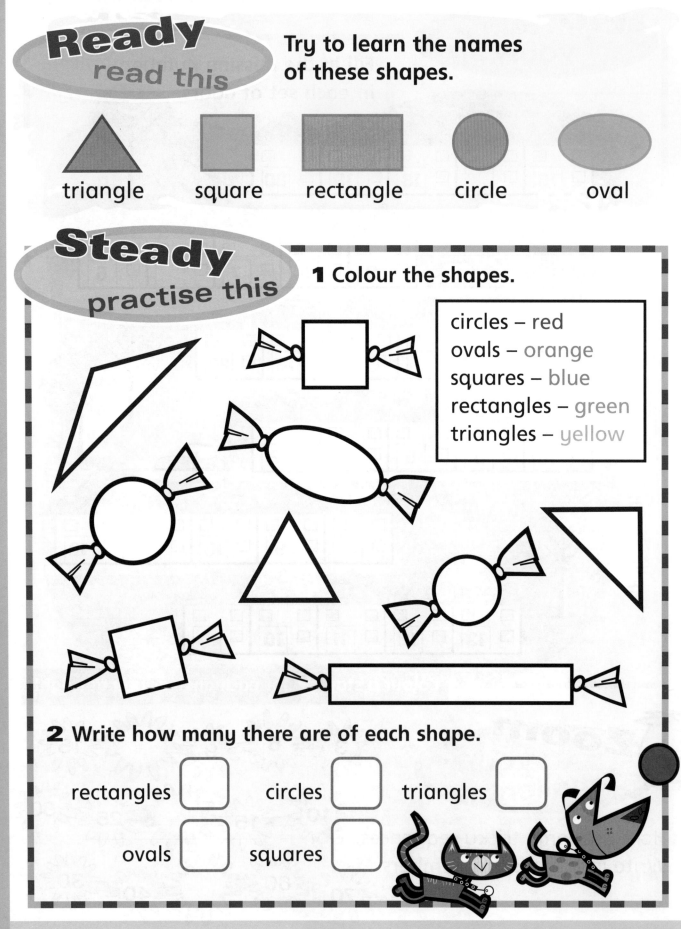

1 Colour the shapes.

circles – red
ovals – orange
squares – blue
rectangles – green
triangles – yellow

2 Write how many there are of each shape.

rectangles ☐   circles ☐   triangles ☐

ovals ☐   squares ☐

Go test yourself

Join these shapes to their names.

1

oval

rectangle

2

3

triangle

4

circle

5

6

square

Colour a star ⭐ for each answer you get right.

Zoom your challenge

Count the different shapes you can see in this picture.

ANSWERS: (1) rectangle; (2) triangle; (3) oval; (4) triangle; (5) square; (6) circle

More and less

A number line can help you work these out.

1 **more than 15 is 16**
10 **more than 15 is 25**

1 **less than 15 is 14**
10 **less than 15 is 5**

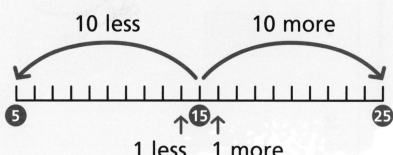

10 less   10 more

5   15   25

1 less   1 more

Steady
practise this

1 Write the correct number for each hook.

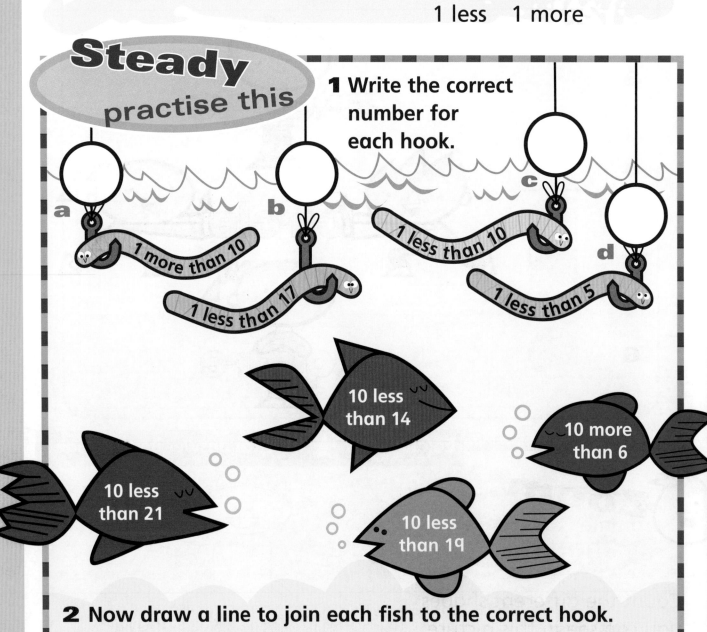

a   1 more than 10

b   1 less than 17

c   1 less than 10

d   1 less than 5

10 less than 14

10 more than 6

10 less than 21

10 less than 19

2 Now draw a line to join each fish to the correct hook.

More and less

Answer these.

1 1 more than 12 is

2 10 more than 18 is

3 10 less than 20 is

4 1 less than 10 is

5 1 less than 17 is

6 10 more than 9 is

Colour a star ⭐ for each answer you get right.

Zoom your challenge

Draw a 1p coin in each purse and write the total.

Draw a 10p coin in each bag and write the total.

9

Finding totals

There are 5 pointed hats and 3 flat hats. Count them to find how many hats there are **altogether**.

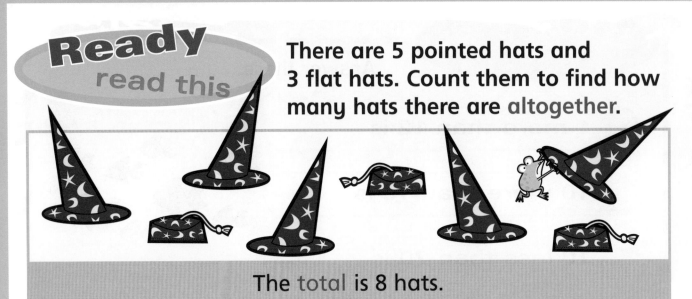

The **total** is 8 hats.

1 Count each type of animal and write the total.

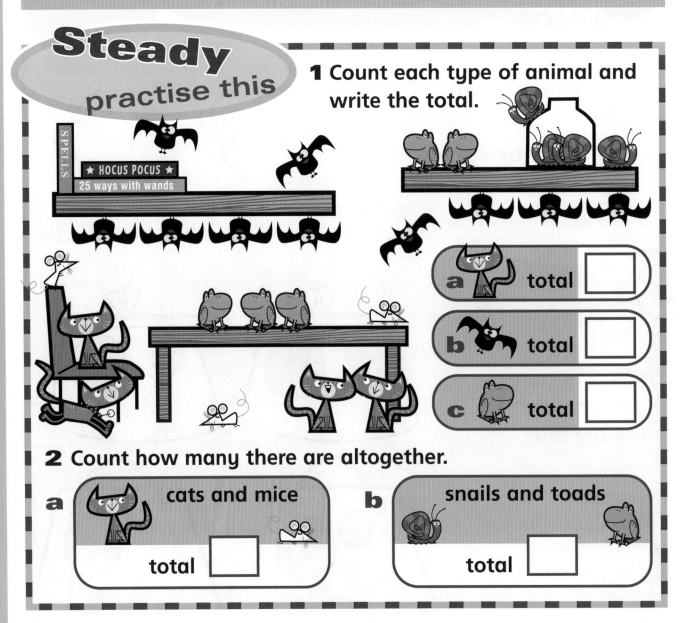

a total [ ]

b total [ ]

c total [ ]

2 Count how many there are altogether.

a cats and mice
total [ ]

b snails and toads
total [ ]

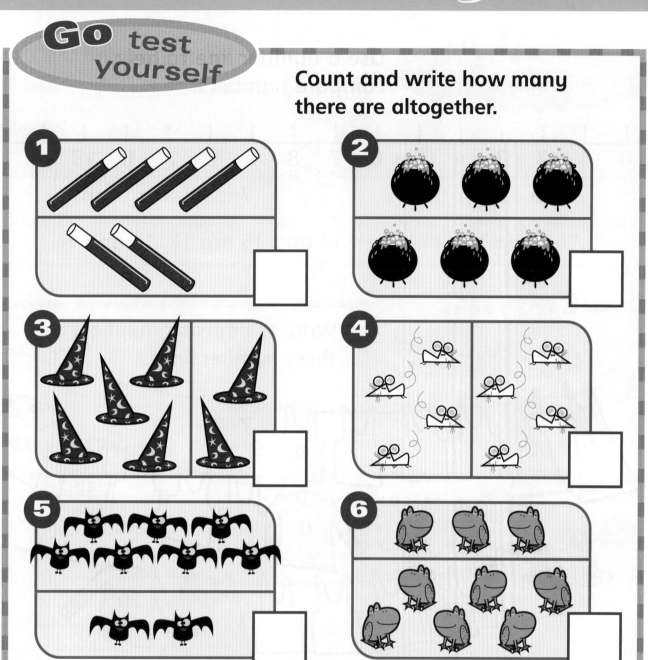

Go test yourself

Count and write how many there are altogether.

1

2

3

4

5

6

Colour a star ⭐ for each answer you get right.

Zoom your challenge

Colour some stars red on each cloak so the total number of red stars is 10.

Comparing numbers

Use a number line to help compare numbers.

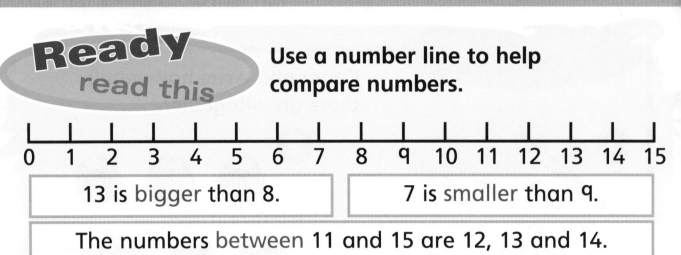

| 0 | 1 | 2 | 3 | 4 | 5 | 6 | 7 | 8 | 9 | 10 | 11 | 12 | 13 | 14 | 15 |

13 is bigger than 8.

7 is smaller than 9.

The numbers between 11 and 15 are 12, 13 and 14.

Steady practise this

1 Write the missing numbers on these number lines.

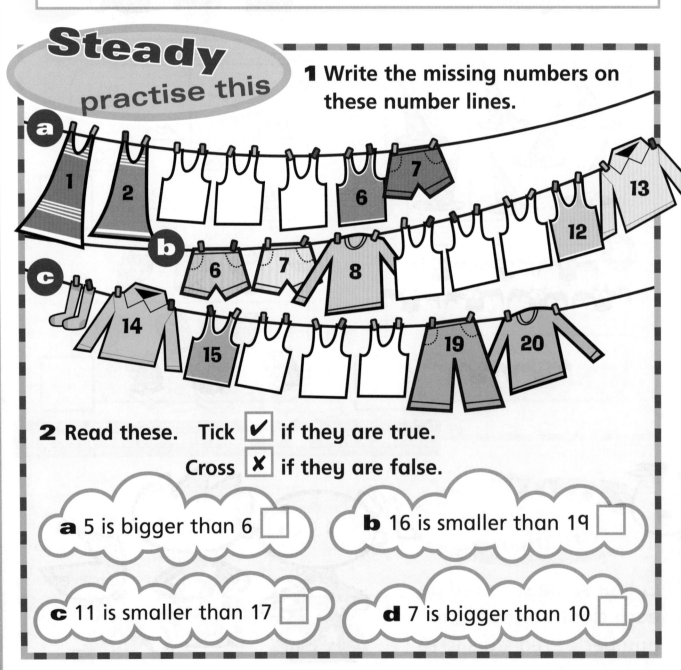

2 Read these.   Tick ✔ if they are true.

Cross ✘ if they are false.

a 5 is bigger than 6 ☐

b 16 is smaller than 19 ☐

c 11 is smaller than 17 ☐

d 7 is bigger than 10 ☐

Comparing numbers

Circle the correct number.

1 Which of these numbers comes between 9 and 12?

8   13   7   11

2 Which of these numbers is smaller than 4?

7   5   3   6

3 Which of these numbers is larger than 17?

14   19   16   12

Circle two numbers that have swapped places.

4   5   6   7   9   8   10

5   12   13   14   17   16   15

6   8   9   12   11   10   13

Colour a star ⭐ for each answer you get right.

Zoom your challenge

Colour **most** of the flowers red. Colour the rest yellow. Write the numbers in the boxes.

☐ red flowers

☐ yellow flowers

ANSWERS: (1) 11; (2) 3; (3) 19; (4) 9, 8; (5) 17, 15; (6) 12, 10

13

Solid shapes

Look around you and try to find shapes like these:

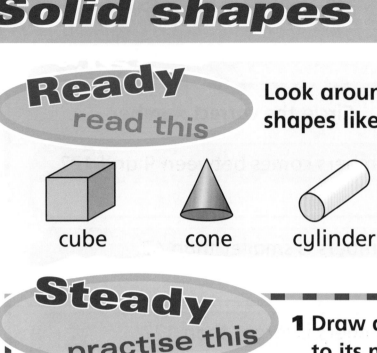

cube   cone   cylinder   cuboid   sphere

Steady practise this

1 Draw a line from each shape to its name.

a

c

e

b

d

cube   cone   cylinder   cuboid   sphere

2 Write how many of each shape you can find.

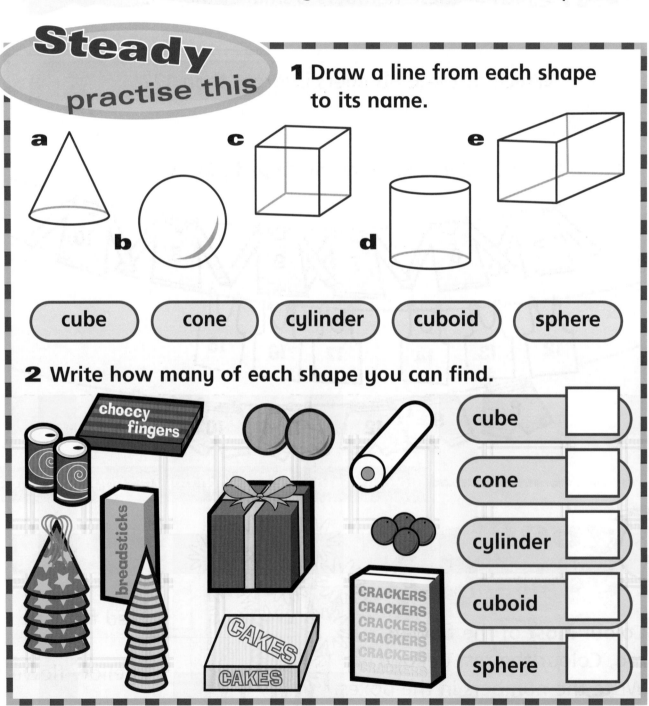

cube

cone

cylinder

cuboid

sphere

ANSWERS: 1 (a) cone; (b) sphere; (c) cube; (d) cylinder; (e) cuboid
(2) cube → 1; cone → 10; cylinder → 3; cuboid → 4; sphere → 6

14

Solid shapes

Circle the correct shape.

1 sphere

2 cuboid

3 cube

4 cylinder

5 cone

6 cuboid

Colour a star ⭐ for each answer you get right.

Zoom your challenge

Go on a cube hunt!

Make a list of the cube shapes that you can find all around you.

Can you find more than 10?

TISSUES

⭐1 ⭐2 ⭐3 ⭐4 ⭐5 ⭐6

15

Finding differences

How many more dogs are there than bones?

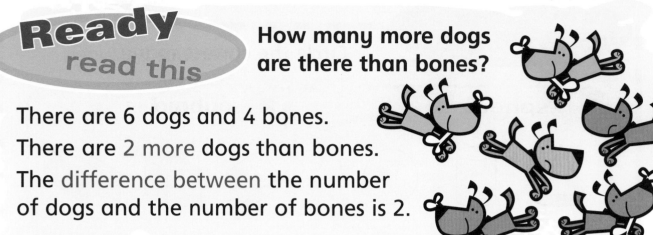

There are 6 dogs and 4 bones.

There are 2 more dogs than bones.

The difference between the number of dogs and the number of bones is 2.

Steady — practise this

1 There are 3 cats. Count how many more of these things there are than cats.

a ☐ more collars

b ☐ more beds

c ☐ more bowls

2 Complete these sentences.

a There are ☐ more bowls than beds.

b There are ☐ more bowls than collars.

Finding differences

Go test yourself

Write the difference between these pairs of numbers.

1 | 4 | 2 | the difference is ☐

2 | 3 | 7 | the difference is ☐

3 | 2 | 5 | the difference is ☐

4 | 6 | 4 | the difference is ☐

5 | 6 | 1 | the difference is ☐

6 | 4 | 7 | the difference is ☐

Colour a star ⭐ for each answer you get right.

Zoom your challenge

Join pairs of numbers with a difference of 5.

8   5   4   9   3   7   2   10

ANSWERS: (1) 2; (2) 4; (3) 3; (4) 2; (5) 5; (6) 3

⭐1 ⭐2 ⭐3 ⭐4 ⭐5 ⭐6 **17**

Measuring

Use real objects to compare length, mass and capacity.

Length
The stripy scarf is longer than the red one.

Mass
Ross is heavier than Alice.

Capacity
The teapot holds more than the cup.

Steady
practise this

1 Join these objects by drawing a line in order of length, from the shortest to the longest.

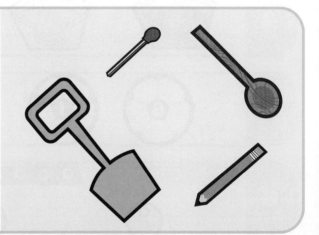

2 Join these objects by drawing a line in order of weight, from the lightest to the heaviest.

ANSWERS: (1) match → pencil → spoon → spade
(2) feather → egg → chicken → corn

18

Measuring

 **Go test yourself**

Tick the correct picture.

Which is longer?

 1

 2

Which is heavier?

 3

 4

Which holds more?

 5

 6

Colour a star for each answer you get right.

Zoom your challenge

You need lots of pennies.

How many pennies do you need to measure the length of this book?

How many pennies do you need to measure your hand span?

How much longer is the book than your hand span?

ANSWERS: (1) bus; (2) settee; (3) book; (4) bike; (5) bucket; (6) saucepan

      19

Ordinal numbers

These are called ordinal numbers. They show the **order** of things.

1st	2nd	3rd	4th	5th
first	second	third	fourth	fifth

Steady practise this

1 Write the order in which these boats will finish the race.

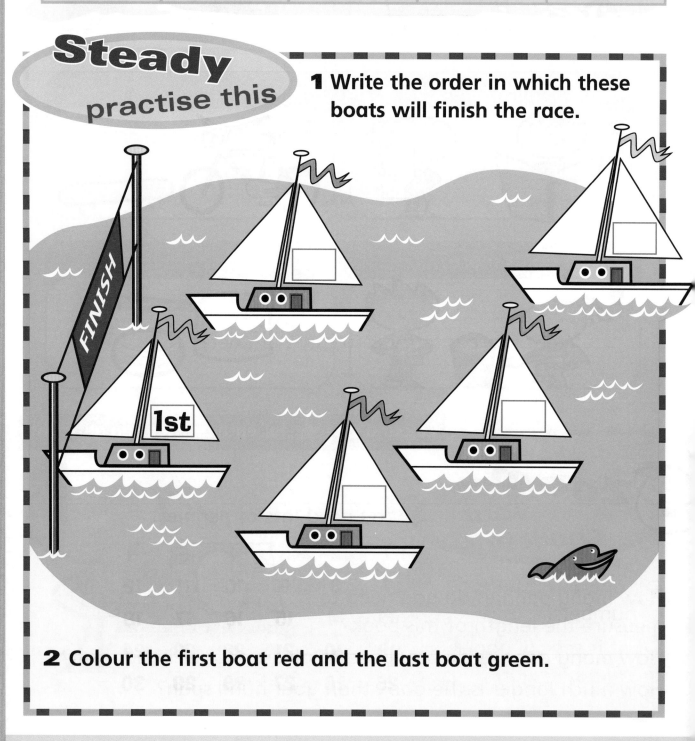

2 Colour the first boat red and the last boat green.

Ordinal numbers

Go test yourself

Look at the alphabet and answer these questions.

A B C D E F G H I J K L M N O P Q R S T U V W X Y Z

1 What is the 3rd letter of the alphabet?

2 What is the first letter after S?

3 What is the last letter of the alphabet?

4 What is the 2nd letter after J?

5 What is the sixth letter of the alphabet?

6 What place is letter D in the alphabet?

Colour a star ★ for each answer you get right.

Zoom your challenge

Colour red the 2nd, 4th and 6th columns of numbers.

What is special about the numbers you have coloured?

1	2	3	4	5	6
7	8	9	10	11	12
13	14	15	16	17	18
19	20	21	22	23	24
25	26	27	28	29	30

ANSWERS: (1) C; (2) T; (3) Z; (4) L; (5) F; (6) 4th

Money

These are some of the coins we use:

1p 2p 5p 10p 20p 50p £1

Add coins carefully to give totals.

2p 2p 5p

The total is 9p.

When you work out change, count on from the price.

This sweet costs 8p.
The change from 10p is 2p

2p

0 1 2 3 4 5 6 7 8 9 10

1 Draw a line from each purse to a matching price tag.

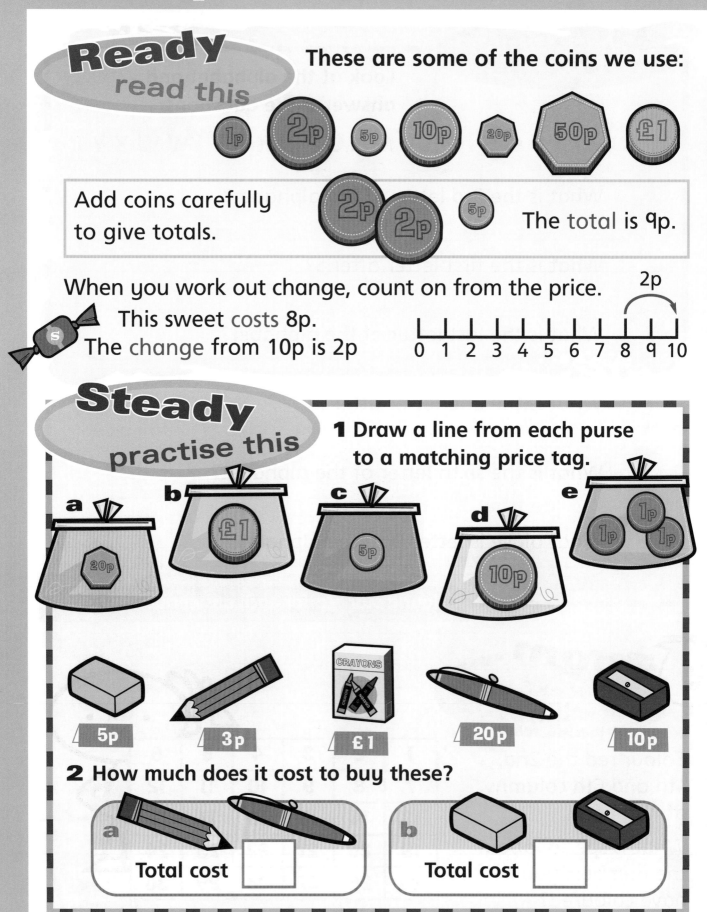

a 20p

b £1

c 5p

d 10p

e 1p 1p 1p

5p

3p

CRAYONS £1

20 p

10p

2 How much does it cost to buy these?

a Total cost ☐

b Total cost ☐

ANSWERS: 1 (a) 20p; (b) £1; (c) 5p; (d) 10p; (e) 3p
2 (a) 23p; (b) 15p

22

Money

Go test yourself

What is the total in each moneybox?

1 10p 1p 5p

2 1p 5p 1p

3 2p 1p 10p

What change from 10p do you get from each of these?

10p

4 7p

5 9p

6 5p

Colour a star ⭐ for each answer you get right.

Zoom your challenge

Four coins are used to pay for this exactly. Draw the four coins.

comic 19p

ANSWERS: (1) 16p; (2) 7p; (3) 13p; (4) 3p; (5) 1p; (6) 5p

23

Time

Ready read this

These clocks show the time to the hour and half-hour.

4 o'clock

half-past 8

Steady practise this

1 Draw a line to match the clocks with the correct times.

a

b

c

d

Dentist half-past 11

Haircut half-past 12

cinema film starts 7 o'clock

LUNCHTIME opens 1 o'clock

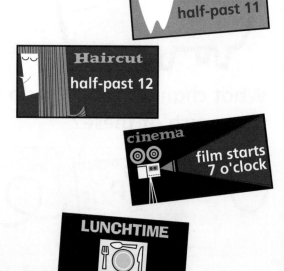

2 These digital clocks show the same times as above. Write in the missing numbers.

a **12:0**

b **1:0**

c **:00**

d **1:30**

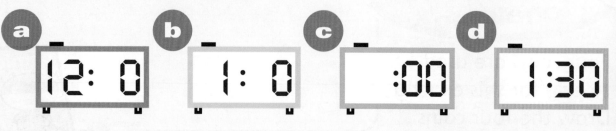

Time

Write these times.

1

2

3

Draw the missing hands on these clocks to show the times.

4

5

6

| 3 o'clock | half-past 5 | 9.30 |

Colour a star for each answer you get right.

Zoom your challenge

Look for different timers and clocks at home. Can you find any of these?

Use a timer to time how long it takes you to carry out a task.

How long does it take you to…

…get dressed?   …write your name five times?

…go into every room in your house?   …make a sandwich?

ANSWERS: (1) 10 o'clock or 10.00; (2) half-past 2 or 2.30; (3) six o'clock or 6.00; (4) ; (5) ; (6)

25

Ordering numbers

Ready read this

Numbers can be put in order.

18 17 19 16
14   15

14 15 16 17 18 19

Steady practise this

1 Write the numbers on these football shirts in order, starting with the smallest.

(12 9 10 7 11 8)

2 Write the names of these sisters in age order, starting with the oldest.

Amita Age 5

Megan Age 12

Sam Age 20

Gemma Age 15

oldest   youngest

Ordering numbers

Write each set of numbers in order, starting with the smallest.

1
20 19
17 18

smallest
☐ ☐ ☐ ☐

2
1 3
4 2

smallest
☐ ☐ ☐ ☐

3
9 10
11 8

smallest
☐ ☐ ☐ ☐

4
8 5
7 6

smallest
☐ ☐ ☐ ☐

5
14 16
13 15

smallest
☐ ☐ ☐ ☐

6
11 12
13 10

smallest
☐ ☐ ☐ ☐

Colour a star ⭐ for each answer you get right.

Zoom your challenge

Put these price labels in order, starting with the smallest amount.

12p   17p   24p   21p
23p   9p   30p

☐ ☐ ☐ ☐ ☐ ☐ ☐

ANSWERS: (1) 17, 18, 19, 20; (2) 1, 2, 3, 4; (3) 8, 9, 10, 11; (4) 5, 6, 7, 8; (5) 13, 14, 15, 16; (6) 10, 11, 12, 13

Adding

Count the oranges to find out the **total**.

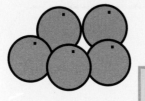
5

4

5 add 4 equals 9.
5 + 4 = 9

Steady
practise this

1 Count how many and write the **total**.

a

☐ + ☐ = ☐

b

☐ + ☐ = ☐

c
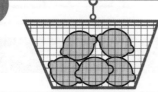
☐ + ☐ = ☐

2 Draw more fruit and write the total.

a 6 + 2 = ☐

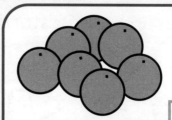
b 7 + 3 = ☐

Adding

Go test yourself

1. 5 + 5 =
2. 6 + 3 =
3. 2 + 7 =
4. 5 + 6 =
5. 4 + 8 =
6. 9 + 4 =

Write the answers.

Colour a star ⭐ for each answer you get right.

Zoom your challenge

Write the missing numbers 1, 2, 3 and 4 in the boxes to complete these.

4 + ☐ + ☐ = 8

5 + ☐ + ☐ = 11

ANSWERS: (1) 10; (2) 9; (3) 9; (4) 11; (5) 12; (6) 13

⭐1 ⭐2 ⭐3 ⭐4 ⭐5 ⭐6 **29**

Taking away

There were 8 balloons.

3 balloons have burst.
That leaves 5 balloons.

8 take away 3 leaves 5.
8 − 3 = 5

Steady practise this

1 Write how many. Take away 2.
How many are left?

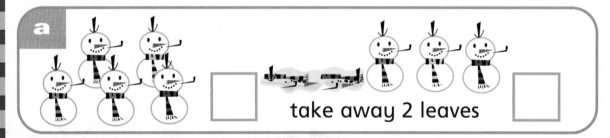

a   take away 2 leaves

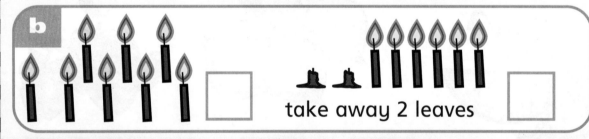

b   take away 2 leaves

c   take away 2 leaves

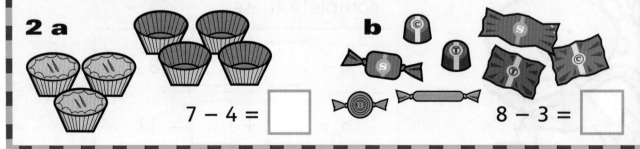

2 a   7 − 4 =

b   8 − 3 =

Taking away

 **Go** test yourself

Write the answers.

1 10 take away 7 leaves ☐

2 6 − 3 = ☐

3 9 take away 8 leaves ☐

4 10 − 4 = ☐

5 11 take away 6 leaves ☐

6 12 − 5 = ☐

Colour a star ★ for each answer you get right.

Zoom your challenge

Join pairs of numbers that have a difference of 6.

ANSWERS: (1) 3; (2) 3; (3) 1; (4) 6; (5) 5; (6) 7

Maths check

Use this page as a quick reference for key maths facts.

Numbers to 20

0 1 2 3 4 5 6 7 8 9 10 11 12 13 14 15 16 17 18 19 20

one	two	three	four	five
six	seven	eight	nine	ten
eleven	twelve	thirteen	fourteen	fifteen
sixteen	seventeen	eighteen	nineteen	twenty

Shapes

triangle　　square　　rectangle　　circle

cube　　cone　　sphere　　cuboid　　cylinder

Days of the week

Monday
Tuesday
Wednesday
Thursday
Friday
Saturday
Sunday